THE BLUE FAIRY BOOK

Edited by Andrew Lang

Student Study Guide

David M. Wright

MEMORIA PRESS
www.MemoriaPress.com

THE BLUE FAIRY BOOK
Edited by Andrew Lang

STUDENT STUDY GUIDE
David M. Wright

ISBN 978-1-61538-387-0

First Edition © 2014 Memoria Press

Cover illustration by Arthur Rackham

Contents

PREPARING TO READ:

REVIEW
- Orally review any previous vocabulary.
- If need be, review fairy tales read thus far.
- Periodically review the concepts of character, setting, plot, and theme.

STUDY GUIDE PREVIEW
- Reading Notes:
  - Read aloud together.
  - This section gives the students key characters, places, vocabulary, and literary terms that are relevant to the particular fairy tale.
- Vocabulary:
  - Have students attempt to determine the right word from the word from the Definitions Bank. It is also helpful to read the vocabulary words aloud together so that students will recognize the words when they come across them in their reading.
- Comprehension Questions:
  - At your discretion, read through these questions (or some) with students to encourage purposeful reading.

READING:
- Students should read the fairy tale (or a section of the fairy tale) independently. The other good option is to have students read sections of the fairy tale aloud.
- For younger students, you can alternate between teacher-read and student-read passages. Model good reading skills. Encourage students to read expressively and smoothly. The teacher may occasionally take oral reading grades.
- While reading, mark each vocabulary word as you come across it.
- Have students take note in their study guide margin of the particular pages where a Comprehension Question is answered.

AFTER READING:

VOCABULARY
- Look at each word within the context that it is used by reading a sentence or two before and after the word. Discuss the definition given in the Definitions Bank. It can also be helpful to discuss some additional synonyms for the word.
- Record the word's meaning in the students' study guides, writing it exactly as it appears in the Definitions Bank. (If possible, use students' knowledge of Latin and other vocabulary in your discussion of the definitions.)

COMPREHENSION QUESTIONS
- Older students can answer these questions independently, but younger students (2nd-4th) need to answer the questions orally, then form a good sentence, and then write it down, using correct punctuation, capitalization, and spelling. (For younger students, you may want to write the sentence down after forming it orally, and then let students copy it perfectly.)
- It is not necessary to write the answer to every question. Some may be better answered orally.
- Answering questions and composing answers is a valuable learning activity. Questions require students to think; writing a concise answer is a good composition exercise.

QUOTATIONS AND DISCUSSION QUESTIONS
- Use the Quotations and Discussion Questions sections of each lesson as a guide to your oral discussion of the key concepts in the fairy tale that may not be covered in the Comprehension Questions.
- These Quotations and Discussion Questions help take the students' understanding of the fairy tale to a higher level than what is covered in the Vocabulary and Comprehension Questions. Use this time as an opportunity to introduce complexity in their thinking. Here you can introduce concepts that the students may not fully understand yet, but would be beneficial for them to begin thinking about.
- A key to the Discussion Questions is in the back of the Teacher Guide. The answers are short; you should elaborate on the answers in your discussion.

ENRICHMENT
- The Enrichment activities include composition, copywork, dictation, research, drawing, poetry, literary terms, and more.
- This section has a variety of activities in it, but the most valuable activity is composition. Your students should complete at least one composition assignment each week. Proof students' work and have students copy composition until grammatically perfect. Insist on clear, concise writing. For younger students, start with 2-3 sentences, and do the assignment together. The students can form good sentences orally as you write them down, and then the students copy them.
- You may find that there is not enough room for composition in the Enrichment section. Two additional lined pages are provided in the back of the study guide for additional space.
- These Enrichment activities can be completed as time and interest allow. Do not feel you need to complete all of these activities. Choose the ones that you feel are the best use of your students' time.

UNIT REVIEW AND TESTS
- There is a quiz covering every two fairy tales.
- On the weeks that have these quizzes, you may want to review early in the week, and then drill it orally a couple of times before giving the quiz at the end of the week.
- The final exam is longer and covers the last two fairy tales.

"You shall have a son, who will never be happy until he finds out that his nose is too long …"

Reading Notes

enchantment	a spell or some kind of magic
Roman nose	a prominent or slightly curved nose
Prince Hyacinth	the son of the King and Princess; He was given a long nose from the enchanter because his father, the King, broke the enchantment of his mother, the Princess.

Vocabulary

Definitions Bank

not able to be comforted

the act of comparing things to see how they are alike or different

terrible; horrible

wonderful; beautiful

1. The Queen was **inconsolable** when she saw this great nose _____

2. they told him all sorts of **dreadful** stories _____

3. But, do what they would, they were nothing by **comparison** _____

   _____

4. The Prince made him a **splendid** present _____

Comprehension Questions

1. In the beginning of the story, what must the King do to break the enchantment of the Princess whom he loves? Does he succeed? _____

   _____

   _____

2. Who appears "as suddenly as a flash of lightning" and snatches the Dear Little Princess away just as Prince Hyacinth is about to kiss her hand? _____

3. What important person does Prince Hyacinth meet on his journey to find the Dear Little Princess?

   _____

   _____

4. Why does she turn out to be so important? _____

_____

5. What happens when Prince Hyacinth says, "Well, it must be admitted that my nose *is* too long!"?

_____

_____

_____

Quotations

"Now, say if you are not very much obliged to me. Much good it was for me to talk to you about your nose! You would never have found out how extraordinary it was if it hadn't hindered you from doing what you wanted to. You see how self-love keeps us from knowing our own defects of mind and body. Our reason tries in vain to show them to us; we refuse to see them till we find them in the way of our interests."

1. Who said this? _____

Discussion Questions

1. For most of the story, Prince Hyacinth thought his nose was the right size, and everyone else's nose was too small. Whom do you think is most to blame for Prince Hyacinth's faulty view of his nose?

2. Why do you suppose the Dear Little Princess was snatched away just as Prince Hyacinth was about to kiss her hand?

Enrichment

1. From the quotation above, can you find the two sentences that teach an important life lesson? With good penmanship, copy the two sentences below.

_____

_____

_____

_____

_____

_____

_____

*"… putting the slipper to her foot, he found it went on very easily,
and fitted her as if it had been made of wax."*

Reading Notes

cinder	a partially burned piece of coal or wood
symbol	something that stands for something else; an object that has a range of meaning or significance beyond itself
godmother	a woman who serves as a sponsor and protector of a child, usually at a baptism

Vocabulary

Definitions Bank

good manners; politeness

surprise; amazement

twisted or turned; not straight

unpleasant; hateful

1. they made her own daughters appear the more **odious** _____

2. Anyone but Cinderella would have dressed their heads **awry** _____

3. She went and sat down by her sisters, showing them a thousand **civilities** _____

_____

4. The **astonishment** her two sisters were in _____

Comprehension Questions

1. Why could Cinderella's stepmother not "bear the good qualities of this pretty girl"? _____

_____

2. List three jobs that Cinderella's stepmother demanded she do. _____

_____

_____

3. As the two sisters were preparing for the ball, "anyone but Cinderella would have dressed their heads awry, but Cinderella dressed them perfectly well." Why do you think Cinderella still dressed them neatly? What does this reveal about her? _____

_____

4. After Cinderella's fairy godmother changes her clothes into the most beautfiul attire, what specific command does she give her? And what will happen if Cinderella breaks the command? _____

_____

_____

5. How does Cinderella treat her sisters when it is discovered that the glass slipper fits her and she is the beautiful lady? _____

_____

Quotations

"There came thither the finest princess, the most beautiful ever was seen with mortal eyes; she showed us a thousand civilities, and gave us oranges and citrons."

1. Who said this? _____

Discussion Questions

1. Why do you think Cinderella's sisters treated her so terribly? Was it just because Cinderella was their stepsister, or something more?

2. Of what significance is the glass slipper? Could the glass slipper be a symbol for something more important or greater?

Enrichment

1. Draw a picture of an object from your childhood that means much more to you than simply the material that the object is made of. In other words, draw a picture of an object that is very special to you!

"See if any one of them is courageous enough, and loves you well enough to come and save your life."

Reading Notes

setting	the time and place of a story
Central Idea	not necessarily the most important thing that happens in a story, but the most important *idea* in the story
lament	to express regret or disappointment

Vocabulary

Definitions Bank

deserted; empty

extreme tiredness; exhaustion

wasteful and careless spending

wise; sensible

1. All that he had left was a little house in a **desolate** place _____

2. even attributed their misfortunes to their own **extravagance** _____

3. but their father, who was more **prudent**, begged them to wait a little _____

4. he was almost exhausted with cold and **fatigue** _____

Comprehension Questions

1. What is the first major misfortune that happens to the merchant and his twelve children? _____

   _____

   _____

   _____

2. What two things does Beauty wish for from her father when he goes on a journey to retrieve his lost ship?

   _____

   _____

3. When the merchant returns home after attempting to retrieve the goods from his ship, what element of

   setting becomes a dangerous obstacle to him? _____

   _____

   _____

4. What does the Beast demand of the merchant? _____

_____

5. What are some of the physical objects that Beauty sees in the castle to indicate that her dreams contain

real and true messages? _____

_____

_____

6. Why does Beauty feel she must return to the Beast after two months? _____

_____

_____

_____

_____

Quotations

"… and in making me happy you will find your own happiness. Be as true-hearted …"

1. Who said this? _____

Discussion Questions

1. What sets Beauty apart from her sisters?

2. What do you think is the most important idea in the story? Could Beauty's dream contain the most
important idea?

Enrichment

1. Copy a passage (a sentence or two) that you feel contains the Central Idea, the most important idea in
the story.

_____

_____

_____

_____

_____

_____

"But you must not sell it unless you can get the hand-mill which stands behind the door for it. When you come out again I will teach you how to stop the hand-mill, which is useful for almost everything."

Reading Notes

wise old man	a wise fatherly figure who often appears as a grandfather, professor, or wizard, etc.; usually moral, kind, and wise, and provides help and guidance
Dead Man's Hall	a place where the souls of those who have not been very good go after death
herring	a silvery fish abundant in coastal waters that is a common food in many parts of the world
pottage	a thick soup or stew

Vocabulary

Definitions Bank

bickered and argued over the price

required; compelled

dangerous; unsafe

harm or trouble

1. and **haggled** and bargained with the man _____

2. he cried as he went by them as if **mischief** were at his heels_____

3. But the brother would not take it until the other paid him three hundred dollars, and that he was **obliged** to do. _____

4. having to sail far away over the **perilous** sea for freights of salt_____

Comprehension Questions

1. When the poor man gets home with the hand-mill, what is the first thing he asks it to grind?

_____

2. *"'Bless me!' said the old woman as one thing after another appeared; and she wanted to know where her husband had got the mill from, but he would not tell her that."*

Why do you think the poor man would not tell his wife where he got the hand-mill when she asked him?

_____

_____

3. What is the rich brother's reaction to the poor brother's banquet feast that he throws for all his friends?

_____

_____

4. What did the women and the mowers meet on their way home for dinner? _____

_____

5. Why does the skipper want the hand-mill so desperately? _____

_____

6. What happened to the skipper? And why is the sea salty? _____

_____

_____

Quotations

"Would to heaven that each of you had a hundred stomachs! Take care that you are not drowned in the pottage!"

1. Who said this? _____

Discussion Questions

1. Did the poor brother *intentionally* not tell his rich brother how to stop the mill? Do you agree with the poor brother?

Enrichment

1. Draw a picture of the hand-mill grinding salt at the bottom of the sea. Use colored pencils so that your picture will have detail and color.

"But you have a heart," said the Queen. "What should you say if anybody wanted to steal that?"

Reading Notes

Queen of the Woods a magic Queen

stately dignified; majestic

zephyrs West winds

Vocabulary

Definitions Bank

extreme edge

made a low, continuing sound

painfully; emotionally

to beg; to ask for earnestly

1. but she cried more **bitterly** than ever _____

2. When she reached it she sat down upon the **brink** to rest _____

3. and the falling water **murmured** the softest music _____

4. Don't keep me in suspense, I **entreat** you; say that you will marry me. _____

Comprehension Questions

1. What is the difference between Felicia and her brother, Bruno?_____

   _____

2. What magical thing does the Queen do to Felicia's pitcher and the water? _____

   _____

3. What does Felicia offer the Queen instead of the pot of pinks? What does this say about her character?

   _____

   _____

4. What did Felicia's mother, the Queen, do to escape from the tower with Felicia? And then where did she

   go, and what did she do with Felicia? _____

   _____

   _____

5. What three unusual things speak to Felicia, which, after the third, cause her to become pale and faint?

_____

6. Whom does Felicia turn out to be? And whom does she marry? _____

_____

_____

Quotations

"Don't imagine that you are the daughter of the poor labourer who brought you up; your mother was a queen who had six girls already, and the King threatened that unless she had a son …"

1. Who said this? _____

Discussion Questions

1. Does Felicia show compassion to Bruno? Do you think she should have?

2. Felicia says, "Ah! madam … I am so happy that I should like everybody else to be happy too." Reflect on her words here. What virtues do they reveal?

Enrichment

1. *"'Ah! madam,' she answered simply, 'if I have your friendship I shall do very well.'"*
When Felicia says this to the Queen of the Woods, she reveals her kindness and humility. She is willing to give up her last possession for the Queen's friendship. Write a paragraph about a good friend who is special to you. Be sure to include descriptive details, and perhaps even a quote of something your friend said (include quotation marks).

_____

_____

_____

_____

_____

_____

_____

_____

_____

"Couldn't you have treated me more carefully? You have torn my thin little coat all to shreds ...!"

Reading Notes

dwarfs	mythological beings that dwell in mountains and in the earth; they are often described as short and ugly
trudge	to walk slowly and laboriously
perceive	to become aware of; to recognize

Vocabulary

Definitions Bank

being unthankful or ungrateful   a cliff or steep ledge

careful; hardworking   trusting; confidential

1. they were the sweetest and best children in the world, always **diligent** and always cheerful _____

   _____

2. they came up to them in the most **confiding** manner _____

3. they had slept quite close to a **precipice** _____

4. The girls were accustomed to his **ingratitude** _____

Comprehension Questions

1. Who do you think the beautiful child in a shining white robe is? And why do you think the child appears

   there when the children wake up? _____

   _____

2. Describe how each person and creature reacts when the bear pokes his head through the door. _____

   _____

   _____

3. From whom does the bear want to protect his treasure? Describe the creature.

   _____

   _____

   _____

4. How do the girls continually free the wicked creature? _____

5. After the children free the dwarf, what does he eagerly reach for each time? _____

_____

6. What connection does the dwarf have with the bear? _____

_____

_____

Quotations

"Dear Mr. Bear, spare me! I'll give you all my treasure. Look at those beautiful precious stones lying there."

1. Who said this? _____

Discussion Questions

1. Why do you think the mother carries the red and white rose trees with her wherever she goes?

2. What vice or character flaw does the dwarf have that makes him so rotten?

Enrichment

1. Draw a picture of the red and white rose trees. In the trunk of the trees, or in one or two of the branches, draw a carving of the girls' names, Snow-White and Rose-Red.

"Am I come hither," said the proud, saucy one, "to serve you with water, pray?
I suppose the silver tankard was brought purely for your ladyship, was it?"

Reading Notes

courtesy   good manners; civility; respect

infinite   limitless or endless

Vocabulary

Definitions Bank

a strong dislike   showed excessive fondness or love

politeness; courtesy   complaining; muttering

1. this mother even **doted** on her eldest daughter _____

2. and at the same time had a horrible **aversion** for the youngest _____

3. to see how far the **civility** and good manners of this pretty girl would go _____

4. So away she went, but **grumbling** all the way _____

Comprehension Questions

1. What are the two character traits of the mother and eldest daughter mentioned in the beginning of

    the story? _____

2. How does the youngest daughter respond to the old woman who asks her for a drink? Quote what the

    daughter says (use quotation marks). _____

    _____

3. Why does the Fairy take the form of an old country woman? _____

    _____

4. What first comes out of the younger daughter's mouth? _____

5. How does the Fairy appear to the eldest daughter, Fanny? How does Fanny respond to her? _____

    _____

6. What comes out of Fanny's mouth when she returns? Whom does her mother blame for this? _____

_____

7. What happens to the younger daughter at the end? _____

_____

_____

Quotations

"Wouldst not thou be glad, my dear, to have the same gift given thee? Thou hast nothing else to do but go and draw water out of the fountain, and when a certain poor woman asks you to let her drink, to give it to her very civilly."

1. Who said this? _____

2. Why did she say this? _____

_____

Discussion Questions

1. Do you think that what comes out of the daughters' mouths is symbolic?

2. Discuss the **title** of the fairy tale. Does it capture what is most important in the tale?

Enrichment

1. Consider what you have learned from this story. Write out some of the ways that we can treat others better. Perhaps people are not always how they appear?

_____

_____

_____

_____

_____

_____

_____

_____

_____

_____

Reading Notes

St. John's Eve The evening of June 23 is the eve of celebration before the feast day of St. John the Baptist, June 24.

simile a comparison of two different things by using *like*, *as*, or *than* (see quote above)

accoutrements equipment; items worn for a particular activity

Vocabulary

Definitions Bank

distant; remote   bet; gamble   healthy growth   sparkled; glittered; shined

1. when the grass was in the height of its **vigor** _____

2. when the youth heard it he was terrified, and went off, running as if for a **wager** _____

3. when evening drew near rambled away to the **outlying** field _____

4. all were so bright that they shone and **glistened** _____

Comprehension Questions

1. *"… and the lad jumped up and took to his heels as fast as he could, and never even looked back, and the barn remained empty that year just as it had been for the last two."*

    Why did the barn remain empty that year just as it had been for the last two? _____

    _____

    _____

2. What happens to the first two brothers when they attempt to spend the night in the barn? _____

    _____

    _____

3. What does Cinderlad see when he survives the night in the barn? Describe in detail. _____

    _____

    _____

4. What does Cinderlad do each time he sees the horse on St. John's Eve? _____

_____

_____

5. Describe the competition that the King sets up in order to offer his daughter's hand in marriage. _____

_____

_____

6. Each time the knight appears, his saddle and armor are of a different metal. What are the three metals?

_____

7. Refer to the definition of **simile** in the Reading Notes and to the quote at the top of page 20. Now, find

two **similes** in the story and write them here. _____

_____

Quotations

"... but he never got the golden apple! He never left the cinder-heap on any of the three days."

1. Who said this? _____

2. Why did they say it? _____

_____

Discussion Questions

1. Why do you think Cinderlad's brothers treat him so rudely?

2. Do you think it is destiny that Cinderlad is able to make it through the night and tame the horses? Or is he simply more courageous?

Enrichment

1. Cinderlad showed a lot of courage in the barn during the rumbling and the earthquake. Imagine that you are in the barn that night. What does it sound like? How do you feel? Would you run away like the other brothers, or would you stay there?

_____

_____

_____

_____

"… and he had really tried to cure himself of these defects, but by that time all his faults had become habits; and a bad habit is very hard to get rid of."

Reading Notes

resolution	a firm decision to do or not do something
churlish	being rude and difficult to deal with
menagerie	a collection of wild animals kept in captivity for exhibition

Vocabulary

Definitions Bank

agreeing to do something

forced to leave a country as punishment

to prevent or stop someone from doing something

renewal; re-establishment

1. they may insult and **thwart** you as often as they please _____

   _____

2. to try and frighten the shepherdess into **consenting** to marry him _____

3. they now had a good opportunity of getting him **banished** for ever _____

   _____

4. let us pity him and hope for his **restoration** _____

Comprehension Questions

1. As an offer to the good King, what three things does the Fairy say she is willing to provide for his son,

   Prince Darling? Does the King ask for any of these three, or something else? _____

   _____

   _____

   _____

2. What object does the Fairy give to Prince Darling as a young boy to help him be good? What does the

   object do? Do you think the object could be viewed as a **symbol** for something that we all have within

   us? What could it be? _____

   _____

   _____

3. Though Prince Darling does not want to admit any wrongdoing in beating his dog, the Fairy points out his three faults. What are they? _____

_____

_____

4. To help correct Prince Darling's thinking, and to instruct him, what does the Fairy say is the true advantage of possessing a great empire? _____

_____

_____

5. What response does Celia give to Prince Darling when he says he wants to marry her? You may summarize what she says in your own words, or quote her directly using quotation marks. _____

_____

_____

_____

6. As a punishment for Prince Darling becoming wicked, what combination of animals does the Fairy turn him into? List each animal and the character trait of Prince Darling that it symbolizes.

_____ – _____

_____ – _____

_____ – _____

_____ – _____

Quotations

"I would return good for evil," he said to himself, "and save the unhappy man's life."

1. Who said this? _____

2. Why is this quote important in the story? What crucial change takes place? _____

_____

_____

Discussion Questions

1. Why do you think the Fairy is referred to as "Fairy Truth"?

2. Why is white the favorite color of Fairy Truth? What do you think white symbolizes?

3. Why do you think Celia is in the cave with an old hermit? What might he represent?

Reading Notes

fret	to worry or be anxious
conscience	the inner sense of what is right or wrong in one's thoughts and actions
dearth	an inadequate amount; a famine
malicious	full of or showing malice, meanness, spitefulness

Vocabulary

Definitions Bank

a skillful action or movement

comforted; made to feel better

expressed disapproval or found fault with

luxurious; magnificent

1. this **maneuver** he repeated again and again _____

2. his conscience had **reproached** him for leaving his children behind _____

_____

3. But he **consoled** his little sister, and said: "Don't cry, Grettel …" _____

4. and laid a most **sumptuous** dinner before them_____

Comprehension Questions

1. What is the stepmother's "solution" for the family's lack of food resources? How does the father feel

    about this plan? _____

    _____

    _____

2. How do Hansel and Grettel first find a way home from the woods? _____

    _____

3. What does it mean that the father's "conscience had reproached him for leaving his children behind"?

    _____

    _____

4. When do the children search for the breadcrumbs on the path? Do they find them? What happened to them? _____

_____

5. Who leads the children to the sugar-and-cakes house? _____

6. How is Hansel able to trick the old woman into thinking that he is not gaining weight? _____

_____

7. How is Grettel able to trick the old woman? What is she able to do to her? _____

_____

_____

Quotations

"These are even better than pebbles," … and crammed his pockets full of them.

1. Who said this? _____

2. Why was this said? What are better than pebbles? _____

_____

Discussion Questions

1. Read aloud the short poem that Grettel calls out to the white duck. Have students memorize the poem.

2. What is your favorite part of this story? Why do you think it is so well known?

3. What do you think is the moral of this story?

Enrichment

1. Draw a picture of the old woman, a picture of the sugar-and-cakes house, or both.